Text Structure

Reading Comprehension Book
Reading Level 3.5–5.0

Introduction

Welcome to the Edupress Text Structure Reading Comprehension Book. This resource is an effective tool for instruction, practice, and evaluation of student understanding. It includes ideas on how to introduce different text structures to students, as well as activities to help teach and practice the concepts.

The reproducible activities in this book are tailored to individual, small-group, and whole-class work. They include leveled reading passages, graphic organizers, worksheets, and detailed instruction pages. These activities provide opportunities to use text, illustrations, graphics, and combinations of these elements to practice cause/effect, compare/contrast, problem/solution, sequence, and descriptive text structures while reading.

The material in this book is written for readers at the 3.5–5.0 reading level. However, the activities can easily be adapted to your students' ability levels and your time frame. After introducing an activity to students, model it by working through one or two examples aloud. You may wish to also read text passages aloud to students, or they can be read silently or aloud by students. For students who need personalized help, individual and small-group activities have been included. These activities can be done alone or with a classroom aide for explicit instruction.

We know you will be pleased with the progress your students make in understanding text structures after using this book.

D1500585

EP2375 © 2013 Demco, Inc. • 4810 Forest Run Road • Madison, WI 53704
ISBN 13: 978-1-56472-325-3

www.edupress.com

Table of Contents

Directions: Introducing Text Structure

Whole Class/Small Group

Make a copy of Text Structure Definitions on page 4 on a transparency, and introduce the concept of text structure to the students. Then, make multiple copies of the Definitions and Text Structure Questions on page 5, and give one of each to each student. Make multiple copies of the text structure articles on pages 6 through 10, and distribute them at random. When students have had an opportunity to read the articles and identify the text structure for each one they received, ask them to find students holding different articles. Encourage them to figure out the differences among the texts.

Individual/Whole Class

To introduce clue words, make a transparency of "The Japan Tsunami" on page 6, and read it as a class. Highlight or underline text structure clue words as you read, such as "as a result." Discuss how clue words helped you figure out the text structure. Encourage students to try the next story independently or with a partner, highlighting clue words. Discuss their findings as a class.

Whole Class ●●●

As you work through your text structure unit, challenge students to find examples of each text structure in textbooks, newspapers, magazines, or any other type of nonfiction text. Help them photocopy the examples; then, read and discuss them as a class. Display examples on a text structure bulletin board, or share examples from the Internet on your class website.

Answer Key

Page 6

"The Japan Tsunami": Cause and Effect

Page 7

"The Rise of Women's Rights": Problem/Solution

Page 8

"Reptiles vs. Birds": Compare/Contrast

Page 9

"The Earthquake of 1906": Sequence

Page 10

"Layers of History": Descriptive

Text Structure Definitions

The Text Structure Secret

Good readers have a secret. They can spot how the information in articles or the events in a story are organized. This is called text structure. Understanding text structure helps the reader focus on the main idea. They understand what they are reading. They also remember more. You can learn this secret, too.

Here are the five basic text structures:

Cause and Effect: The author tells why something happened.

Sometimes, the writer tells about one cause with many effects. For example, if a ball goes over the fence (cause), it may roll into the street, be hit by a car, and pop (effects).

Other times, the author tells about several causes for one effect. For example, if Sara stays up late (cause) and skips breakfast (cause), she will be sleepy in class (effect). Often, the author will write about just one cause with one effect.

Problem/Solution: The author presents a problem. Then, he offers possible solutions. He tells what might happen if each solution is chosen. Finally, he describes the best solution. He tells why he thinks it is the best. For example, an author might write an article about how to fix a leaky sink. He will tell about the different ways to fix it and what the results might be for each one. Finally, he describes the best way to fix the sink and why he thinks it is the best.

Compare/Contrast: The author tells how things are the same or different. These things can be events, places, things, ideas, animals, or even people. For example, an author might write an article comparing a horse to a zebra.

Sequence: The author uses a series of events. The events can be listed in different ways. They can be listed in order of importance, or they can tell what happened first and what happened next. The listing of events leads to a conclusion. If the events are ordered by when they happened, the times can be listed in years, days, hours, or seconds.

Descriptive: The author describes the topic. She names characteristics and features. She uses examples. If she is writing about a zebra, she might talk about its black and white coat, its size, its teeth, and its mane.

Text Structure Questions

Cause and Effect:

What is the cause?

What is the effect?

Is there more than one cause and effect?

What is the result?

What is the reason the result happened?

Problem/Solution:

What is the problem?

What are the solutions?

Who worked to solve the problem?

Has the problem been solved or will it be solved in the future?

Compare/Contrast:

What things are being compared (people, animals, places, objects, events, or ideas)?

How are they alike?

How are they different?

What are the most important similarities or differences?

Sequence:

How are the steps organized? (in the order they happened, step by step, etc.)?

What is the time span of events?

What do the events describe?

Do the events describe a process?

Descriptive:

What person, idea, event, or thing is being described?

Which detail seems to be the most important?

Can you tell how the author feels about what he or she is describing?

The Japan Tsunami

Under the ocean, off the coast of Japan, part of Earth's crust is on the move. The Pacific plate is sliding under the North American plate. This is happening all the time. The movement is very slow. Therefore, only scientists with special tools can detect it.

In some places, the plates stick. Consequently, tension builds up. The tension in these spots can build for more than 800 years. The effect of this build-up is a powerful release. Suddenly, parts of these plates lurch past one another. The result is an earthquake.

This happened on Friday, March 11, 2011. The Pacific plate jolted the ocean floor near Honshu. This led to the release of a huge amount of energy. In turn, this caused energy waves to rush out from the break. They traveled through the rocky crust.

Because these waves rolled through land under Japanese villages and cities, millions of people experienced earthquakes. The trembling ground caused buildings to sway. The tremors caused windows to shatter. Because shelves are not meant to be shaken, everything crashed to the floor. As a result, thousands of possessions were turned to rubble.

Luckily, Japan had a warning system. As a result, many lives were probably saved. Because sensors detected approaching waves, people in Tokyo had a minute to find shelter. Since they were used to earthquakes, they knew what to do. The city of Tokyo was hundreds of miles from the center of the quake. Therefore, it was not damaged as much as towns on the coast.

The movement under the seabed caused a wave to travel through the ocean, too. This enormous wave was called a tsunami (soo-nah-mee). It was 128 feet high when it struck the Omoe peninsula.

Because sea walls were built for lower waves, this one surged over them. As a result, sea water washed away homes, hospitals, and schools. Due to strength, luck, and quick thinking, some people were able to reach high ground. Since there was so little time, others were not able to escape.

Clue Words

caused, in order to, since, as a result, before, reasons why, for this reason, because, so, so that, why, this led to, consequently, the effect of, the result is, therefore, due to

The Rise of Women's Rights

In the 1800s, women had a problem. They had very few rights. There was not much hope for a solution. Since women could not go to most colleges, professions were closed to them. They could not even vote.

Because men controlled money and property, working was not the answer. Some women worked in factories or taught in country schools. The trouble was that these jobs did not pay very much. But that was not the only difficulty. If a woman worked, then the money she earned belonged to her husband, her father, or her brother.

Before the Civil War, special groups of people started forming. They were called *abolitionists* because they wanted to abolish (do away with) slavery. Since many women in the North wanted to see slaves freed, they joined these groups.

In spite of their fears, they stood up and spoke in meetings. Threats of ridicule did not stop them. They spoke out so that slavery would come to an end.

Their courage was a key to future rights for women. Nobody had allowed them to speak before, so they had kept their ideas to themselves.

When women stood up to talk, something changed. Some people made fun of them, but others listened. The speakers realized that they had important things to say. Some went on to become famous writers and speakers. Many began asking questions about their rights as human beings.

Two of these women were Lucretia Mott and Elizabeth Cady Stanton. They believed that people needed to work together for women's rights. The problem was how to make this happen. One solution was to gather everyone for a discussion. The result of their efforts was a meeting in 1848. It was about rights for women. It was called the Seneca Falls Convention.

Organizing the meeting was a challenge. Leaders knew that if everyone just talked, then nothing would be decided. In order to guide the discussions, a group of women wrote a Declaration of Sentiments before the convention. It expressed their feelings about the rights of women. The convention did not solve any of the problems women faced. However, it did mark the beginning of the struggle for women's voting rights.

Clue Words

in spite of, so, problem, changed, because, hopeful, so that, if/then, answer, struggle, threat, worry, one reason for, solution, solve, since, difficulty, question, future, possibility, need, key, way out, result, puzzle, trouble, riddle, in order to, unfortunately, however, changed

All reptiles and birds are animals that have certain things in common. Both reptiles and birds have lungs. They breathe air. Both groups of animals get their energy the same way. They eat other living things. Both groups also move with their own energy.

These qualities make reptiles and birds different from plants. Unlike animals, plants make their own food with energy from the sun. They do not eat other living things. Plants can neither breathe nor move around on their own.

Like mammals, fish, and amphibians, both reptiles and birds are vertebrates. That means they have backbones and skeletons inside their bodies. This separates them from animals like insects and spiders that support their bodies with exoskeletons.

Fish, amphibians, and insects lay eggs. Reptiles and birds lay them as well. In this way, they differ from mammals, which give birth to live young.

Birds and reptiles are the same in many ways, but they are also different. Reptiles like turtles, lizards, and snakes are covered with scales. These little plates protect them. Although not all birds can fly, they all have feathers. Neither birds nor reptiles have fur or hair. That separates them from mammals.

Another difference between birds and reptiles is the way they control their body temperature. On the one hand, reptiles depend on the heat of the sun to warm their bodies. Insects, amphibians, and fish also need the heat of the sun. Birds, on the other hand, are warm-blooded. They create their own heat. In that respect, they are similar to mammals.

The dinosaurs were reptiles. Many of them were much larger than any reptiles living now. Today's reptiles are from a different family than the dinosaurs. Many scientists believe that birds are the closest living relatives of dinosaurs.

Like birds and reptiles of today, dinosaurs hatched from eggs. Like dinosaurs, birds have scales: birds have scales on their feet, and experts say that feathers are made of the same material as scales. Dinosaur skeletons are like bird skeletons in many ways. In fact, scientists are calling all living birds "avian dinosaurs." That means there is little difference between birds and reptiles after all.

Clue Words

both, yet, just like, but, different, same as, unlike, also, too, on the contrary, on the one hand/on the other hand, however, even though, similarly, although, alike, either/or, neither/nor, just as, as well, in comparison, difference, while, more, less, bigger, larger, faster, all, separates them from, in common, stronger, differ, as well

The Earthquake of 1906

Before dawn on Wednesday, April 18, 1906, the people of San Francisco were jolted awake. Their beds and even walls of their rooms were shaking. As soon as they could stand, parents grabbed their children.

Then, they headed for doorways. There had been a number of earthquakes during the previous year, so they knew what to do. The rattling died down, but a few seconds later, at 5:12 a.m., it returned.

The shaking this time was much harder. Floors and ceilings rippled like the sea. Next, dishes, pictures, and sculptures crashed down and shattered. Then, brick chimneys trembled and groaned before crashing through roofs into bedrooms. Outside, electrical poles keeled over and wires sparked on the cobblestones until they went dead. The quake continued for 42 seconds.

As soon as they could, frightened men and women rushed into the streets. Some had stopped to pull on warm pants and coats. Many were still in their night clothes.

Between aftershocks, people went back into their homes. They grabbed money, jewelry, blankets, clothes, food, and cooking supplies.

They did not stay. When they tried their taps, there was no water. There was no gas for heat or for their kitchen stoves. There was no power, and the phones were all dead. Most people set up camp on their porches or their steps. They were ready to dash into the street when the earth began to roll again.

After the shaking stopped, people surveyed the damage. Many homes on firm ground in the hills were not badly damaged. After making sure their families were safe, store owners, doctors, ferry operators, and emergency personnel headed down to the business district. They had to walk because none of the trolleys were running. They knew there would be damage, but they were not ready for what they saw.

Some buildings were tilting at crazy angles. The fronts of others had fallen into the street. All of the show windows were broken. The worst, however, was yet to come. Smoke was starting to rise in many places around the city. Fires were every-where, and the water mains were broken.

(See photographs and read first-hand accounts of this disaster online at "The Virtual Museum of the City of San Francisco" at www.sfmuseum.org)

Clue Words

continued, went on, stopped, paused, first, second, third, next, while, after, when, today, date, then, last, during, until, soon, now, since, finally, time, following, between, before, at this point, as soon as, previous, had been, will be, seconds, minutes, hours, days, years, and specific dates or times (such as 3:15 p.m. or May 1, 2013)

Layers of History

When standing next to the rim of the Grand Canyon, it is possible to see millions of years of Earth's history.

For instance, the rocks deepest in the canyon are the oldest. They include the Vishnu Schist and the Zoroaster Granite. These layers are very dark in color. Scientists estimate that they are more than 1,700 million years old.

Lying on top of these ancient rocks is the Unkar Group. The five layers in this formation are more colorful. They include grays, bright oranges, deep reds, and even purples. The upper layer in this group, the Cardenas Lavas, is dark brown.

Resting on top of the Unkar Group is the Chuar Group. The lower layers are green and the upper layers are tan. Fossils of blue-green algae have been found in these rocks.

The next formation up is the Tonto Group. The three layers of dark sandstone, greenish shale, and gray limestone are about 500 million years old. The hard brown sandstone forms a table-like platform along the walls of the canyon.

Above the Tonto Group sits the famous Redwall Limestone. It is one of the easiest rock layers to identify. It is very thick. Its vertical cliffs are huge. In most parts of the canyon, they are more than 400 feet high. They look deep red, but the crimson color is just a stain on the surface. The limestone is actually brown. In some parts of the canyon, caves and arches form in this layer. It contains many fossils from ancient seas, including clams, corals, and fish.

The next layer, the Hermit Shale, is rusty red. It was laid down when the area hosted damp, shady forests. Climbers have found the tracks of prehistoric reptiles and amphibians in this layer. It is softer than other rocks in the canyon and erodes easily. It forms slopes and causes rock falls.

The Coconino Sandstone is easy to spot near the canyon rim. It is cream-colored or white because it is pure sand. Hikers, who see it up close, notice that it is made of sand dunes turned to stone.

The top two layers of the Grand Canyon are light-colored limestone. They are about 250 million years old. They hold fossils from warm, shallow seas.

Clue Words

such as, is like, next to, beside, above, across, below, under, large, fast, for example, include, show, showing, on top of, along, for instance, in front of, parts, made up of, have, colors, beautiful, numbers, smells, shapes, textures, sizes (huge, tiny, deep, tall), orientation (vertical, horizontal, tilted, flat), age (old, young, new, ancient)

Individual ●

Give each student a copy of Finding Text Structure in Sentences on page 12, and challenge them to name the text structure for each sentence. You may want to display the Definitions sheet from page 4 on a transparency as a reference. Tell students that there are two sentences for each text structure (for example, two sequence, etc.).

Small Group ● ●

Copy Text Structure Topics on page 14. Cut the topics apart, and place them in a bag. Invite each student to choose a topic from the bag. Then, challenge each student to write one sentence on his or her topic using each type of text structure. Tell them to copy their sentences onto the Blank Sentence Strips from page 13. Then, instruct students to choose a partner and match their partner's sentence strips to the correct text structures. For extra practice, have each group choose two sentences and write a paragraph on each. Invite groups to share their paragraphs with each other.

Whole Class ● ● ●

Collect all of the sentence strips from the small-group activity and place them in a bag. Divide the class into two teams. Invite one student from each team to come to the front of the room. Draw a strip from the bag, and read it aloud. The first student to identify the text structure correctly earns a point for his or her team.

Answer Key

Finding Text Structure in Sentences (Page 12)

1. Descriptive
2. Cause/Effect
3. Sequence
4. Cause/Effect
5. Compare/Contrast
6. Descriptive
7. Compare/Contrast
8. Problem/Solution
9. Problem/Solution
10. Sequence

Finding Text Structure in Sentences

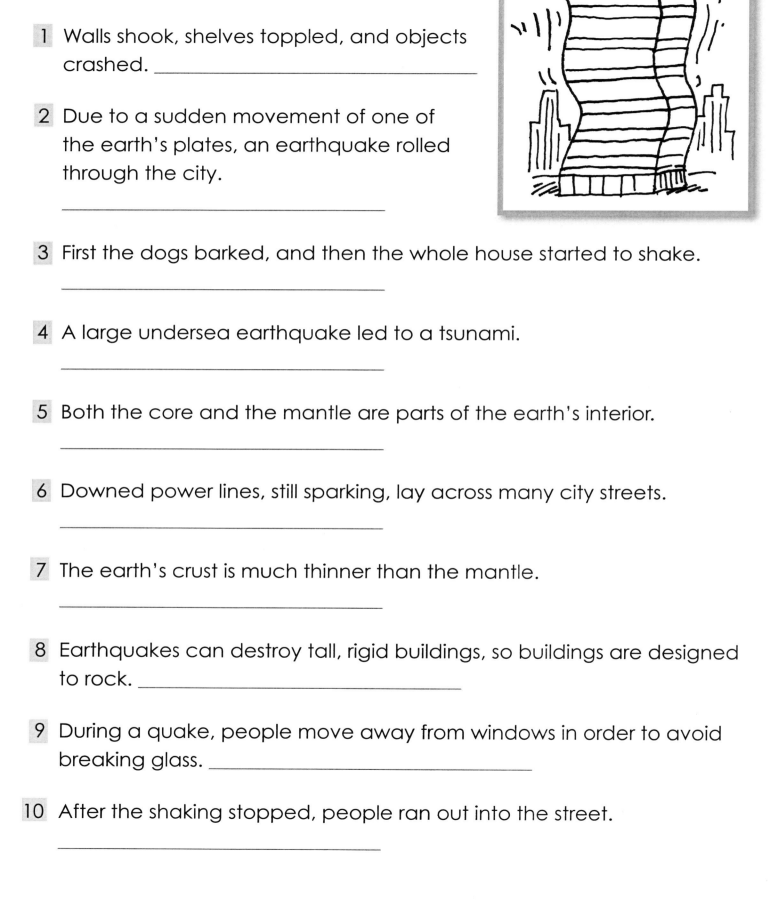

1 Walls shook, shelves toppled, and objects crashed. _____

2 Due to a sudden movement of one of the earth's plates, an earthquake rolled through the city.

_____

3 First the dogs barked, and then the whole house started to shake.

_____

4 A large undersea earthquake led to a tsunami.

_____

5 Both the core and the mantle are parts of the earth's interior.

_____

6 Downed power lines, still sparking, lay across many city streets.

_____

7 The earth's crust is much thinner than the mantle.

_____

8 Earthquakes can destroy tall, rigid buildings, so buildings are designed to rock. _____

9 During a quake, people move away from windows in order to avoid breaking glass. _____

10 After the shaking stopped, people ran out into the street.

_____

Blank Sentence Strips

Cause and Effect

Problem/Solution

Compare/Contrast

Sequence

Descriptive

Text Structure Topics

a storm	a country
a state	a city
a trip	a school or college
a computer, tablet, or cell phone	a movie
a baseball game	a person you admire
a favorite book or story	an event in history
an event in your own life	a real or imaginary animal
The Fourth of July	Thanksgiving
President's Day	Memorial Day or Labor Day
a birthday	a hero
a tragedy or disaster	a fire
a flood	an accident
a personal loss	a lie or deception
a wrong you have forgiven	a victory
a celebration	an escape

Directions: Descriptive Details

Small Group

Divide the class into small groups. Give each group paper and crayons, enough for each student. Read a descriptive paragraph from Visualizing Details on page 16 to the class. Encourage students to individually draw what they see in their minds as you read. Slowly read the paragraph a second time to allow students to finish their drawings and add details.

When finished, invite students to compare their drawings. Did everyone include the same details? Did they see it the same way?

Repeat the activity with the second descriptive paragraph.

Individual/Small Group

Reproduce and cut apart the topics on the Description Topics sheet on page 17. Place the slips in a bag. If you wish, decorate the bag with a picture of a mysterious old house. Reproduce the Alphabet Descriptions page on page 18 for each student.

Allow each student, in turn, to draw a topic slip out of the bag. Caution them to keep their selections secret. Challenge them to write as many descriptive words as possible on their Alphabet Descriptions page. They should try to include one word or phrase for each letter. Each word or phrase must relate to the topic they chose.

When they are finished, have students exchange papers with selected partners. The words and phrases on the list should enable the partner to guess the topic.

Later, encourage students to use the words they wrote to compose poems about their topics.

Individual/Small Group

Make a copy of the Word Map Graphic Organizer on page 19 for each student. Students may either select a topic from the Description Topics page or write about themselves.

Encourage students to fill in the center with the topic or their name. Then, they should fill in the connecting spaces with descriptions of the topic or of themselves. Finally, instruct them to write a descriptive paragraph using the information on the graphic organizer.

For extra practice, have students repeat the activity. Invite them to interview partners or family members instead of writing about themselves.

Visualizing Details

Abraham Lincoln's First Home

Abe was born in a log cabin in Kentucky on February 12, 1809. The cabin had just one room. It was surrounded by open land and trees. There were no other cabins near the Lincoln cabin.

It was probably about 18 feet long and 16 feet wide. There was one door and one window in the front. Early settlers did not have glass. They hung greased paper, quilts, or animal skins in their windows to keep out winter winds. The floor had no wood or carpet. It was hard dirt. On one end of the cabin stood a chimney. The fireplace served for cooking and to keep the family warm.

A replica of the little log cabin is housed inside a large granite shrine at the Abraham Lincoln Birthplace National Historic Park. The building has columns and looks like a temple. It has 56 steps to represent Lincoln's age when he died. It also has 16 windows because he was the sixteenth president.

Mr. Carter's Room

It was like every other classroom in the school. There was a large whiteboard in the center of the front wall. Mr. Carter kept three erasers on the aluminum rail at its base. He was very neat, so they were evenly spaced. There was one on the far left, one exactly in the middle, and one on the far right edge of the rail.

There were two bulletin boards in the front of the room. One of them was on the right side of the whiteboard and the other was on the left. The one on the right side displayed four paintings of mountains. That had been their art lesson on Friday. They were lined up two by two in the middle of the board. The bulletin board on the left side displayed six essays from their writing lesson on Tuesday. Of course, they were lined up in two perfect rows of three each.

Mr. Carter's desk faced the class so he could watch what was going on at all times. It was right in front of the whiteboard, but it was lower, so it didn't block the view. The desk was made of golden oak. There was nothing on top of it except a science text, a laptop computer, and a brown coffee mug containing two sharp pencils, a black marker, and a pen.

Description Topics

your backpack	a doctor's office
your favorite shirt	a department store
your favorite dinner	a car you like
a room you like	an interesting bird
a time of day	an imaginary creature such as a dragon, unicorn, or elf
your pet or a friend's pet	a library you have visited
a famous person	a park you have visited
a special tree	your block or street
a frightening or fascinating house	the most beautiful place you have ever seen
an interesting wild animal	a baby
a garden flower	a very old person
a spider or reptile	a hospital room
an animal that lives in the ocean	a cemetery
a sunset	a jewelry store
your favorite toy when you were little	a bakery

Alphabet Descriptions

A _____

B _____

C _____

D _____

E _____

F _____

G _____

H _____

I _____

J _____

K _____

L _____

M _____

N _____

O _____

P _____

Q _____

R _____

S _____

T _____

U _____

V _____

W _____

X _____

Y _____

Z _____

Word Map Graphic Organizer

Name:_____

Directions: Focus on Sequencing

Whole Class/Small Group ●●●/●●

Make several copies of the first Out-of-Order Sequences paragraph on page 21. Cut apart the sentences, and place each set on a different table in the room. Then, divide the class into groups. Give groups a set amount of time (three to five minutes) to put the sentences in the correct order. Reward the groups that put the paragraph in the correct order.

Next, display a transparency of the paragraph, and model how to find the first sentence and figure out which sentences come next/last. Number the sentences as you determine which one comes next in the sequence.

Then, display a copy of the Sequencing Graphic Organizer on page 22 and fill it in as a class, writing down the steps in the correct order.

Finally, divide the class into partners. Give a copy of the second Out-of-Order Sequences paragraph and a graphic organizer to each pair of students. Challenge them to use the graphic organizer to arrange the paragraph's sentences in the correct order. Encourage them to compare their results with another set of partners.

Individual/Small Group ●/●●

Reproduce the Sequence Topics page on page 23, and cut apart the topics. Ask each student to draw a topic out of a bag.

Tell students that they are going to write directions for their topics. Invite students to work individually or with partners to brainstorm all of the necessary steps. Encourage them to pretend they are talking to someone from another planet. (In other words, they should assume that the other person knows nothing at all about the topic.) When they have listed the steps, instruct them to use clue words such as first, next, then, and last to turn their ideas into a sequential paragraph. Invite them to share their results with the class.

Answer Key

Out-of-Order Sequences (Page 21)

One night in 1613, about 1,500 people were watching a play in the Globe Theater. During the performance, a cannon fired. At first, nobody noticed the spark that landed on the straw roof. During the show, it smoldered. After a while, smoke billowed up. Next, bright flames appeared. Finally, someone spotted the fire and people headed for safety. Although the theater burned to the ground that night, it was rebuilt the next year.

First, the boater puts on his life jacket. Second, he carries the canoe from his car to the shore. Third, he lowers his slender craft into the lake. After he climbs in, he settles into position and picks up the paddle. Next, he lowers the paddle into the water. When he pulls back on the paddle, the canoe glides forward. Then, he lifts the paddle out of the water. Finally, he moves the paddle forward to prepare for his next stroke.

Out-of-Order Sequences

Next, bright flames appeared.

Finally, someone spotted the fire and people headed for safety.

Although the theater burned to the ground, it was rebuilt the next year.

During the performance, a cannon fired.

After a while, smoke billowed up.

One night in 1613, about 1,500 people were watching a play in the Globe Theater.

During the show, it smoldered.

At first, nobody noticed the spark that landed on the straw roof.

Then, he lifts the paddle out of the water.

Finally, he moves the paddle forward to prepare for his next stroke.

Next, he lowers the paddle into the water.

Third, he lowers his slender craft into the lake.

Second, he carries the canoe from his car to the shore.

First, the boater puts on his life jacket.

After he climbs in, he settles into position and picks up the paddle.

When he pulls back on the paddle, the canoe glides forward.

Sequencing Graphic Organizer

1

2

3

4

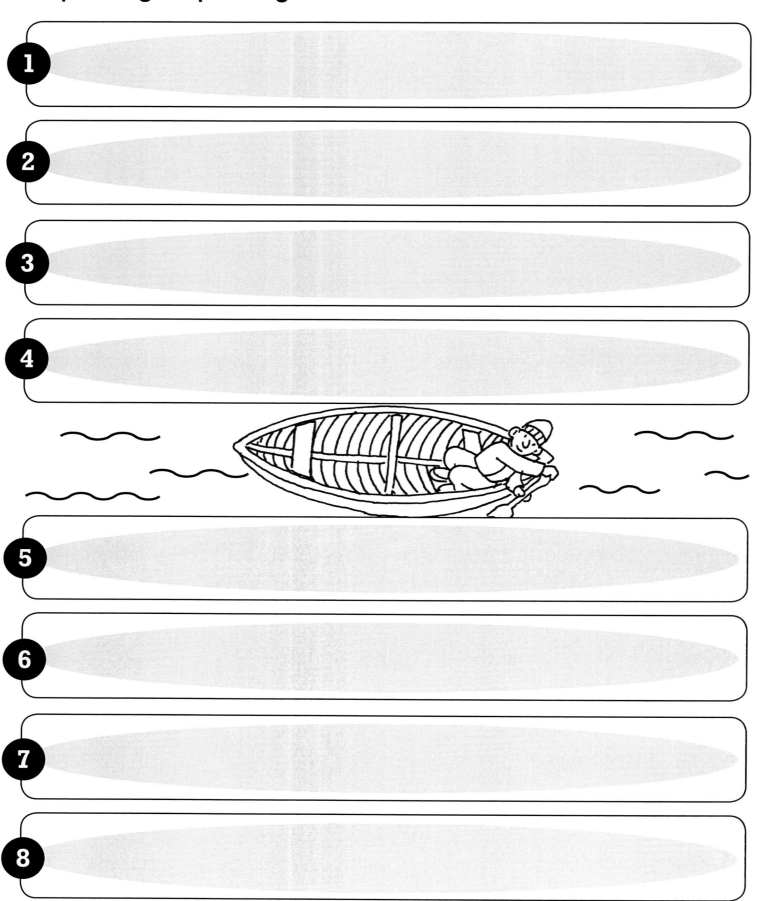

5

6

7

8

Sequence Topics

a volcanic eruption

the formation of a metamorphic, sedimentary, or volcanic rock

the movement of blood through the human body

the movement of oxygen through the human body

the formation of a cloud, rain, or snow

planning a party or celebration

contacting a friend on a phone or other device

surviving a fire or other home disaster

preventing a home fire

preventing an athletic injury

preventing the flu or a cold

washing your hands correctly

planning a sleepover or a road trip with a friend

riding a bicycle, a skateboard, or snowboard

making your favorite smoothie

making toast or your favorite breakfast

making your favorite lunch

eating ribs, chicken drumsticks, or some other messy food

cleaning up after an art lesson

hitting or catching a baseball or softball

making a basket in basketball or a goal in soccer

feeding a dog, cat, or other pet

growing a great garden

sewing on a button or fixing something

cooling off on a hot day

making a greeting card for a family member

estimating the cost of items in a shopping cart

waking up on time

packing for a trip

planning a great Saturday

Directions: Biographies

Individual

Give each student a copy of Mixed-Up Biographies on page 25, the Biography Graphic Organizer on page 26, and two copies of the Biography Timeline on page 27. Instruct students to read the Mixed-Up Biographies and fill in the graphic organizer. Discuss their results as a class. What clues helped them put the events in order?

Individual/Small Group ● / ●●

On a separate sheet of paper, have students write down eight events in their lives (e.g., born in 2002, got a dog in 2005, had fifth birthday party at a zoo, etc.). Then, tell them to write a paragraph or two describing their lives, using clue words such as first, then, after, etc.

On a transparency of the Biography Timeline, show students how to place these steps on a vertical timeline. Then, divide the class into pairs, and give each student a copy of the timeline. Instruct the partners to exchange paragraphs. Then, tell each student to fill in the timeline with events from his or her partner's life.

Whole Class ●●●

Show students how to fold several sheets of paper together and staple the middle to form booklets. Then, challenge each student to illustrate the pages of his or her book with events from his or her life, one event per page in chronological order. Have them label each illustration with the date it took place and a brief description. Invite all students to share their timeline booklets with the class.

Answer Key

Laura Ingalls Wilder (Page 25)

Laura Ingalls was born on February 7, 1867, in Wisconsin.

She married Almonzo Wilder on August 25, 1885.

Nearly a year and a half after their wedding, their daughter, Rose, was born.

Soon after moving to Missouri in 1894, they bought their farm, Rocky Ridge.

In 1911, Laura began writing for a magazine, the *Missouri Ruralist*.

Twenty years after Laura started writing for the magazine, *Little House in the Big Woods* was published.

After the publication of her first book, Laura became a bestselling author and finished writing the Little House series.

In 1957, Laura died at Rocky Ridge Farm.

George Washington (Page 26)

George Washington was born on February 22, 1732, in Virginia.

He married Martha Custis on January 6, 1759.

In 1774, he became a delegate to the First Continental Congress.

On June 15, 1775, he became the head of the Continental Army.

He signed the Declaration of Independence on July 4, 1776.

On April 30, 1789, he became the first president of the United States.

In 1796, after serving a second term as president, he published his Farewell Address.

He died at his home, Mount Vernon, on December 14, 1799.

Mixed-Up Biographies

Laura Ingalls Wilder

Twenty years after Laura started writing for the magazine, *Little House in the Big Woods* was published.

Soon after moving to Missouri in 1894, they bought their farm, Rocky Ridge.

Laura Ingalls was born on February 7, 1867, in Wisconsin.

In 1911, Laura began writing for a magazine, the *Missouri Ruralist*.

In 1957, Laura died at Rocky Ridge Farm.

After the publication of her first book, Laura became a bestselling author and finished writing the Little House series.

Nearly a year and a half after their wedding, their daughter, Rose, was born.

She married Almonzo Wilder on August 25, 1885.

George Washington

He signed the Declaration of Independence on July 4, 1776.

In 1774, he became a delegate to the First Continental Congress.

George Washington was born on February 22, 1732, in Virginia.

On April 30, 1789, he became the first president of the United States.

On June 15, 1775, he became the head of the Continental Army.

He married Martha Custis on January 6, 1759.

He died at his home, Mount Vernon, on December 14, 1799.

In 1796, after serving a second term as president, he published his Farewell Address.

Biography Graphic Organizer

Name:_____

Birth

4th important event

1st important event

5th important event

2nd important event

6th important event

3rd important event

Death

Biography Timeline

Name

Year	1st important event
Year	2nd important event
Year	3rd important event
Year	4th important event
Year	5th important event
Year	6th important event
Year	7th important event
Year	8th important event

Directions: Problem/Solution Practice

Whole Class

Reproduce Problem/Solution Matching 1 and 2 on pages 29 and 30. Cut the problems and solutions apart, and place them in a bag. Make sure that you have a problem or solution for each student. Ask each student to take one slip.

Tell the students to find the person who has either the matching problem or solution. They will need to move around the room and consult with other class members.

When everyone has found a match, invite the partners to read their slips aloud. Did they find the correct matches? Ask the class to agree or disagree.

Whole Class/Small Group

Make a transparency of Find a Solution on page 31, and discuss it with the class. Ask for possible solutions to each problem, and discuss which would be best. Work through a few together, and then challenge partners or small groups to finish the sheet. Encourage the partners or groups to share their answers with the class.

Individual/Small Group

Reproduce "The Dams of Port Angeles" on page 32 for each student, and have them fill in the graphic organizer from page 33 with one (or more) of the problem/solutions in the story. Then, challenge them to think of a different solution to the problem than the one in the story and write it in their graphic organizer. Encourage them to partner with someone and compare their alternative solutions. Were they the same or different? Then, ask students to think of a time when they had a problem. Invite them to fill in the graphic organizer with their problem and their solution. Could they have solved their problem in another way? Encourage them to write a few paragraphs describing the problem and the solution.

Answer Key

Problem/Solution Matching 1 (Page 29)

1. Matt couldn't find anything on his desk./He organized everything on his desk.
2. Ariel had trouble waking up on time./She asked for an alarm clock.
3. Jake needed $20 to sign up for the team./He earned money by mowing lawns.
4. Ava was hungry after school./She made a sandwich.
5. Pablo outgrew his old jeans./He went shopping at a clothing store.
6. Brianna's family needed more space./Her family had a yard sale.
7. Pete wasn't good at catching./He asked his dad to throw balls to help him practice.
8. Anna wanted to be a lifeguard./She took swimming lessons.
9. Drake wanted to be an artist./He drew and painted every day.
10. Jacob's dog was lost./He put a lost dog advertisement in the newspaper.
11. Kelly wanted to be an actress./She tried out for a play.
12. Andy had a toothache./He went to the dentist.

Problem/Solution Matching 2 (Page 30)

1. Darren was failing math./He went to a math tutor.
2. Rico had to write a paper./He went to the library to do research.
3. Emily wanted to play an instrument./She took guitar lessons.
4. Becca's friends were not nice to her./She made friends with other girls.
5. Steve wasn't a good batter./He practiced batting with a machine.
6. Anita often fell asleep in class./She started going to bed earlier.
7. Logan couldn't read the board./He went to the eye doctor.
8. Dara's skin burned easily./She wore sunscreen when she went outside.
9. Mosquitoes bit Tim on hikes./He wore insect repellant.
10. Mia didn't like her hairstyle./She got a new haircut.
11. Dominic always forgot his homework./He put his homework in his backpack.
12. Casey couldn't do a cartwheel./She asked the gymnastics coach for help.

Problem/Solution Matching 1

Problems

Matt couldn't find anything on his desk.

Ariel had trouble waking up on time.

Jake needed $20 to sign up for the team.

Ava was hungry after school.

Pablo outgrew his old jeans.

Brianna's family needed more space.

Pete wasn't good at catching.

Anna wanted to be a lifeguard.

Drake wanted to be an artist.

Jacob's dog was lost.

Kelly wanted to be an actress.

Andy had a toothache.

Solutions

He earned money by mowing lawns.

She took swimming lessons.

He asked his dad to throw balls to help him practice.

He drew and painted every day.

She asked for an alarm clock.

He put a lost dog ad in the newspaper.

She tried out for a play.

He went to the dentist.

He organized everything on his desk.

He went shopping at a clothing store.

Her family had a yard sale.

She made a sandwich.

Problem/Solution Matching 2

Problems

Darren was failing math.

Rico had to write a paper.

Emily wanted to play an instrument.

Becca's friends were not nice to her.

Steve wasn't a good batter.

Anita often fell asleep in class.

Logan couldn't read the board.

Dara's skin burned easily.

Mosquitoes bit Tim on hikes.

Mia didn't like her hairstyle.

Dominic always forgot his homework.

Casey couldn't do a cartwheel.

Solutions

She wore sunscreen when she went outside.

He wore insect repellant.

He practiced batting with a machine.

He put his homework in his backpack.

She asked the gymnastics coach for help.

She took guitar lessons.

She got a new haircut.

He went to the eye doctor.

She made friends with other girls.

He went to the library to do research.

He went to a math tutor.

She started going to bed earlier.

Find a Solution

1 You miss a friend who has moved away.

_____

2 A friend loses his glasses.

_____

3 A new student seems lonely.

_____

4 You are so mad you feel like throwing something.

_____

5 You can't think of a project for the science fair.

_____

6 You can't think of a question to ask a guest author.

_____

7 You need extra help with long division.

_____

8 There is a lost dog on the school playground.

_____

9 You are giving an oral report and you are nervous.

_____

10 Your best friend won't talk to you.

_____

11 You break your mom's favorite dish.

_____

12 A bully is teasing you.

_____

13 You spill paint all over your new t-shirt.

_____

14 You get sick at school.

_____

15 You forget your lunch money.

_____

The Dams of Port Angeles

Port Angeles is a coastal town in the state of Washington. In the early 1900s, the state was growing fast. It did not have enough wood for building or paper for business.

When developers spotted the forests around town, they saw a chance to solve that problem. Those trees could be changed into things people would buy. Sawmills would process wood products. A new railroad would take them to market. They faced another problem, though. They needed electricity to do all of this.

In 1910, a power company offered a solution. They built the Elwha Dam. For a while, the dam made more than enough power for the area. But that did not last long, because the lumber business kept growing.

Shops sprang up to serve loggers and their families. Soon they needed more electricity. Another company came to the rescue. They built a second, bigger dam in 1927.

The power companies solved the problem of electricity, but they created other difficulties for the future. Some people had jobs in the lumber industry. Other people depended on fishing.

Before the two dams were built, there were plenty of fish. Each year, about 380,000 wild salmon struggled up the Elwha River so that they could lay their eggs at the head of the stream. If they could not swim all the way up the river, then they would not lay their eggs. Because the dams blocked their path, fewer fish came. By the 1990s, only about 3,000 salmon made the trip.

Meanwhile, Port Angeles changed. Much of the area became a national park. Shops and hotels served tourists. Wildlife and natural beauty were the area's new treasures. But these assets were threatened by the dams.

In addition, the dams were getting old. Some worried that they might break. Because they no longer met the power needs of the area, they were not worth fixing.

For these reasons, officials decided to remove both dams. The project has already begun. It will be finished soon. Then, the river will flow free. Ecologists are hopeful about the future of the valley.

The Elwha dams solved the problems of the early 1900s. Today's problems are not the same. Every period in time has its own challenges. As problems change, people must look for new answers.

Problem

Solution

Alternative Solution

Directions: Cause and Effect Practice

Whole Class/Small Group ●●●/●●

Introduce the concept of cause and effect to students. Reproduce Missing Causes and Effects on page 37 on a transparency. Complete the first three or four together as a class, talking about the cause and effect relationship for each.

Divide the class into pairs. Give each pair a copy of the Missing Causes and Effects page. Have them fill in the remaining missing effects and missing causes.

As an extension, challenge each student to choose one or two of the causes and effects to illustrate. Encourage partners to describe to each other the cause and effect relationships in the pictures.

Individual/Small Group ●/●●

Reproduce Cause and Effect Match-Up on page 36 for each student. Tell students to draw lines matching the cause to the correct effect. Then, encourage them to find a partner and check each other's work.

Whole Class ●●●

Reproduce Cause and Effect Charades on page 35, cut apart the effects, and place them in a bag. Divide the class into two teams. One at a time, invite students from each team to come forward, draw an effect from the bag, read it silently, and act it out. The actor's team states a cause/effect relationship that makes sense. (The cause can be anything that makes sense with that effect. For example, the cause for "You cheer" could be "Your team scored a point," "You found out you won a prize," etc.) If the actor's team members have not guessed a cause and effect that makes sense within a certain time limit, the opposing team can guess.

Answer Key

Cause and Effect Match-Up (Page 36)

1. k
2. i
3. p
4. f
5. g
6. j
7. o
8. e
9. b
10. l
11. a
12. d
13. m
14. n
15. c
16. h

Missing Causes and Effects, Suggested Answers (Page 37)

1. It was autumn.
2. It had snowed.
3. It was very cold outside.
4. She broke her arm.
5. It stormed last night.
6. A storm was coming.
7. He went to bed very late.
8. A volcano erupted.
9. The ground is muddy.
10. A forest fire starts.
11. The fire is put out.
12. People got sick.
13. Bears must hibernate.
14. The eggs will hatch.
15. The *Titanic* sank.
16. My plants grow big.

Cause and Effect Charades

You scream, tremble, and then point off to one side.

You listen and then laugh.

You beg by putting your palms together, and bounce up and down nervously.

You thrust both hands into the air over your head and mouth, "Yes!"

You shake your head from side to side, put both palms in front of you facing out, and mouth, "No, no, no!"

You sniffle and use your fists to rub your eyes.

You pant and bend at the waist, gasping for breath.

You shiver, fold your arms across your chest, and rub your upper arms with your hands.

You cover your eyes with your fingers.

You put one hand in front of you to signal "stop!"

You applaud.

You shrug your shoulders and put both hands out to the side, palms facing the ceiling.

You wipe your forehead with your hand and then fan yourself.

You screw up your face and hold your nose.

You "eat" something, make a face, and pretend to spit it out.

You tiptoe across the room.

You yawn.

You open your mouth and both eyes wide.

You tilt your head to the right, and then scratch it with your right index finger.

You shade your eyes with your hands.

You lick your lips and rub your tummy.

You whisper a secret to someone.

You look up, put out a hand, palm facing the ceiling, cover your head and then run.

You raise a hand and wave it excitedly.

You sneeze.

You listen on a phone and scribble furiously on a piece of paper.

Cause and Effect Match-Up

1 Sara took care of her plants.

2 Marco mowed lawns to earn extra money.

3 Ann kept her books too long.

4 Aaron overslept.

5 Terri put off writing her report.

6 Shawn was bitten by gnats.

7 A strong wind blew.

8 The power went off.

9 It was over 100 degrees outside.

10 Chan ran up a steep hill.

11 The snow melted fast.

12 The colonists won the war.

13 Sophia was walking home when it started to pour.

14 The railroad was finished.

15 Liz read more books.

16 Tara forgot her sweater.

a. Melt water filled the river.

b. People stayed inside where it was cool.

c. She became a better reader.

d. The colonies became independent.

e. The lights didn't work.

f. He got to school late.

g. She ran out of time and handed it in late.

h. She was shivering.

i. He could pay for his trip.

j. He couldn't stop scratching.

k. She had a healthy garden.

l. He was out of breath.

m. She put up her hood and ran.

n. People could travel by train.

o. Branches fell into the street.

p. She had to pay a library fine.

Missing Causes and Effects

What is the cause?

1. The maple leaves turned red and orange. _____

2. The roads were slippery. _____

3. The lake was frozen. _____

4. She had to wear a cast for several weeks. _____

5. In the morning, the streets were blocked by fallen tree branches. _____

6. Thunder rumbled overhead. _____

7. He could hardly keep his eyes open the next day. _____

8. A lava flow covered the town. _____

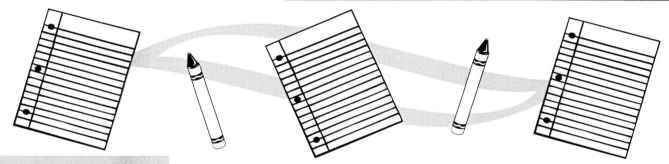

What is the effect?

9. Snow melts in the mountains. _____

10. A hiker fails to put out his campfire. _____

11. Firefighters hose down a burning house. _____

12. Europeans brought diseases to the New World. _____

13. There is little for bears to eat in the winter. _____

14. A mother bird keeps her eggs warm. _____

15. The *Titanic* hit an iceberg. _____

16. I water my garden every night. _____

Directions: Little Causes, Big Effects

Give each student a copy of "A Happy Reunion" on page 39 and the Cause and Effect Graphic Organizer on page 40. Challenge students to read the story and fill in the graphic organizer with as many cause/effect relationships as they can find in the story. Instruct them to use the back of the sheet if they run out of space. Then, invite students to partner up and compare their graphic organizers.

Encourage students to write their own cause and effect stories, using at least three different cause and effect examples. Have them begin by choosing a topic, such as My Dog. Then, have them write their cause/effect examples before writing their story. For example, "My dog was dirty, so I gave him a bath. My dog hates water, so he ran away. Because my dog didn't come right back, I had to go look for him." Then, tell students to pair up, trade stories, and fill in the graphic organizer for their partner's story. Partners should discuss their graphic organizers. Did each student find all of the cause/effect relationships?

Answer Key (Suggested Answers)

"A Happy Reunion" (Page 39)

1. Jacob's family moved to Wisconsin; he had to leave his best friend.
2. Jacob and Raymond were lonely; they made new friends.
3. They were busy; they lost touch with each other.
4. Jacob needed books; he walked down the street to the library.
5. A woman dug through her purse frantically; her pen fell out.
6. Jacob wanted to help; he scooped up the pen and gave it to the woman.
7. The driver started to close the door; she yelled "Wait!"
8. She was about to cry; her voice faltered.
9. She forgot her wallet; she would be late.
10. Jacob knew how she felt; he gave her some money.
11. She was grateful; she said, "You saved my life."
12. Jacob never saw her again; he didn't know what happened next.
13. Jacob was kind to the woman; she made it on time.
14. She was not late; she had time to practice her answers.
15. She had time to practice; she was confident.
16. She was confident; she landed a position in the 911 operator training program.
17. She didn't want Jacob's favor to be wasted; she spent hours studying.
18. She worked hard; she scored the highest on the test.
19. She earned a high score; she got an operator's job.
20. She acted quickly; she saved the motorcycle rider's life.
21. He was glad to be alive; he founded a website for friends to find each other.
22. Raymond had moved away; Jacob couldn't find him.
23. Raymond found Jacob on the Long Lost Friends website; he emailed Jacob.
24. Jacob helped a stranger; he and Raymond found each other again.

A Happy Reunion

Jacob's family moved from California to Wisconsin when he was 10 years old. He had to leave behind his best friend, Raymond. Jacob and Raymond were lonely. As a result, they made new friends at school. Because they were busy with their new lives, they lost touch with each other.

One day, Jacob needed some books for a school report, so he walked down the street toward the public library. A bus roared past him and pulled up to a stop nearby.

A woman at the bus stop started digging through her purse frantically. As a result, a pen clattered to the sidewalk. In order to help, Jacob scooped it up and handed it to her.

"Are you okay?" he asked.

Because the driver started to close the door, she turned and yelled, "Wait!"

Then, her voice faltered because she was about to cry. "I forgot my wallet, so now I'll be late."

Jacob knew how she felt. For that reason, he reached into his pocket and pulled out some money. He handed it to her. She turned as she boarded the bus. Because she was grateful, she said, "You saved my life." Since Jacob never saw her again, he didn't know what happened next.

A few minutes later the woman stepped off the bus in front of the city Emergency Services building. Due to Jacob's kindness, she made it on time.

Since she was not late, she had a chance to practice her answers to the interview questions. Therefore, when the elevator door opened to the office on the fifteenth floor, she was confident. Because of her poise, she landed a position in the training program for 911 operators.

She didn't forget how Jacob had helped her. She didn't want his favor to be wasted. Therefore, she spent hours studying. Due to her hard work, she scored the highest on the test at the end of the course. This led to an operator's job.

One night, she was answering calls when a witness reported a motorcycle accident. She sent out the police and the paramedics, and she told the caller how to help the injured rider. Her quick action saved the rider's life. When the man recovered, he was so glad to be alive that he decided to do something meaningful with his time. For this reason, he founded a website where friends who have lost touch can try to contact each other.

When Jacob was in college, he decided to try to contact Raymond. But Raymond had moved away and Jacob couldn't find him. Then one day, Raymond e-mailed Jacob. He had found him on the Long Lost Friends website! Jacob never knew it had happened because he helped a stranger at a bus stop.

Cause and Effect Graphic Organizer

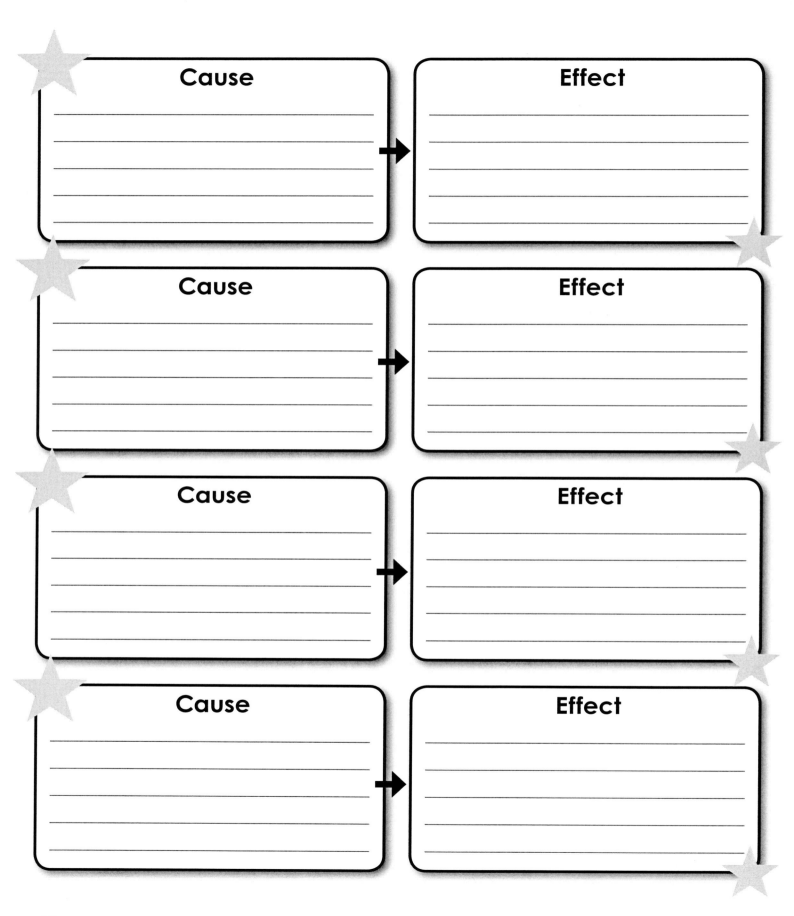

Cause

Effect

Cause

Effect

Cause

Effect

Cause

Effect

Directions: Compare/Contrast Practice

Whole Class

Copy "Sun and Moon" on page 42 on a transparency. As a class, review the clue words that help identify a compare/contrast story (such as both, but, same, different, etc.). Point out that comparative forms of describing words such as "more," "less," and "bigger" also signal comparisons and contrasts. Then, read the story aloud.

Ask students what main things the article is comparing (sun and moon). Ask whether other things are compared, too. (Objects in space are compared.) Ask students to identify some of the clue words in the article and highlight them on the overhead. Ask students to identify things that are similar and different about the topics. Use one color to underline things that are similar; use another color to underline things that are different.

Small Group

Separate students into groups. Copy the Compare/Contrast Pairs on page 43, cut them apart, and place them in a bag. Have each group draw a compare/contrast pair from the bag. Give a Compare/Contrast Venn Diagram from page 44 to each group member. Model how to fill it in. Instruct students to complete the diagrams independently. Give them time to research their topics, if necessary. Then, encourage students to share the information they wrote in each diagram section with their group.

Tell each student to circle the information on their diagram if someone else in the group also wrote it down. Invite them to discuss any information that only one person thought of. Encourage them to add it to their diagrams if they all agree. Finally, ask whether anything else could be added.

Individual

Have students use their Venn Diagrams from the small-group activity to write a compare/contrast paragraph about their topic. Encourage them to illustrate the two things they are comparing. As an extension, challenge students to write a short compare/contrast poem. For example, they might write one about hawks and owls, using terms they listed on their diagram.

Sun and Moon

The sun and moon are bodies in space. These two objects are similar in some ways and different in others.

The sun and moon are both members of our solar system. Both are spherical (ball-shaped). Each rotates (spins) around an axis, and each has a north and south pole.

Both have gravity. Similarly, both are pulled by the gravity of other objects, so each revolves in an orbit. The sun revolves around the center of the galaxy. The moon revolves around Earth. The orbit of each is elliptical (oval-shaped).

The moon, like Earth, is terrestrial. That means it is made of rock. This makes it the same as some objects in the solar system and different from others. Mercury, Venus, and Mars are also made of rock. In comparison, the larger planets and the sun are made of gas.

The sun and the moon seem similar. They both shine in the sky. Looking up, they both look round, and they seem to be about the same size. However, they are not as alike as they appear.

First, the sun is much larger than the moon. It is about 865,000 miles across, while the moon is only 2,160 miles across. That means the sun is more than 400 times larger than the moon. The sun is more than 100 times larger than Earth. In fact, the sun contains more than 99% of all the matter in our solar system.

The sun and moon only seem to be the same size because distant objects look smaller. Although the moon is about 240,000 miles from Earth, the sun is almost 93 million miles away.

In addition, the sun and moon send light to Earth in different ways. On the one hand, the sun is a star. Burning gases inside it shoot out light and heat in all directions. On the other hand, the moon is a rocky object. Unlike the sun, it does not make heat or light. It just reflects light.

The sun and the moon belong to different categories. The sun is a star, while the moon is a satellite. There are seven other planets in the solar system. Some of them have several satellites. Our solar system has only one star, but there are billions of stars in our galaxy, the Milky Way.

Compare/Contrast Pairs

biography and autobiography	a calendar and a clock
fruits and vegetables	a galaxy and a solar system
robins and ducks	the moon and planets
lizards and dinosaurs	lakes and rivers
turtles and snails	sandstone and granite
science and science fiction	diamond and coal
trains and trucks	dolphins and sharks
stars and planets	vultures and eagles
wood and paper	buffalo and cattle
glass and steel	soccer and hockey
television and radio	mystery and fantasy stories
automobiles and bicycles	pizza and spaghetti
clocks and sundials	basketball and football

Compare/Contrast Venn Diagram

Topic 1

Both

Topic 2

Directions: Text Structure Articles

Make copies of Text Structure Articles 1, 2, and 3 from pages 46 through 48 on transparencies. Divide the class into two teams. Using a different color for each team, give each student a colored index card. Display one article. The first student to figure out the text structure for each article should write it on his or her card in pencil and hold it up. If the answer is correct, the student earns a point for his or her team. The team can earn bonus points if the student explains how he or she identified the text structure (clue words, etc.).

After the game, discuss as a class how the same topic can be written about using different text structures.

Assign each student or pair a topic, or allow them to choose from the list on page 14. Give students time to research their topic. Then, challenge them to write two different short articles on their topic, each in a different text structure. After they finish, encourage students to partner up and identify the text structure for each of their partner's articles. They should notice the differences between the two articles.

Answer Key

Text Structure Articles 1 (Page 46)

"No-Hitters: A Special Feat": Cause/Effect

"Cy Young Makes History": Sequence

Text Structure Articles 2 (Page 47)

"The Power of Electricity":
Problem/Solution

"Comparing Electricity" :
Compare/Contrast

Text Structure Articles 3 (Page 48)

"The Islands of Hawaii": Descriptive

"Hawaiian Volcanoes": Sequence

No-Hitters: A Special Feat

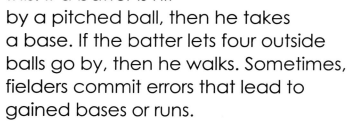

In baseball, the pitcher is very important. If batters can't hit pitched balls, then they can't score. As a result, a great pitcher wins games for his team.

A no-hitter that allows no points is a perfect game. For this reason, every pitcher dreams of one. Since this is difficult in the major leagues, it does not happen all the time. Because baseball is unpredictable, the number of no-hitters changes each season.

No-hitters are not always perfect games. Strangely, a pitcher can pitch a no-hitter and still allow the other team to score points. There are several possible reasons for this. If a batter is hit by a pitched ball, then he takes a base. If the batter lets four outside balls go by, then he walks. Sometimes, fielders commit errors that lead to gained bases or runs.

Consequently, it is possible to pitch a no-hitter and still lose the game. Because most points are driven by hits, this is very rare. As a result, it has happened only twice in the history of the game.

Cy Young Makes History

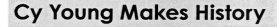

Cy Young was the first to pitch a perfect game with modern rules. It was May 5, 1904. More than 10,000 baseball fans gathered in Boston. They had come to see the Boston Americans play the Philadelphia Athletics.

The Philadelphia pitcher had beaten Young on April 25. After the game, the unsportsmanlike winner taunted the loser in interviews. This was a bitter rematch. Everyone wanted to see what would happen.

The first inning was fast. Each Athletics batter came up to the plate. Then, each one went back to the bench. Soon, three outs sent the team to the field.

The second inning was the same. The third inning also left the Athletics without hits. By the sixth inning, the Boston players were excited. They started staying away from Young. They didn't want to jinx his no-hitter.

They didn't have to worry. The seventh and eighth innings were hitless for the Athletics. When the ninth inning began, the crowd was cheering. Young struck the first two batters out. The last was his rival, the pitcher. Finally, Young struck him out, too.

Young went on to pitch more hitless games in an amazing winning streak. He still holds the National Baseball League record.

Text Structure Articles 2

The Power of Electricity

Today, we are struggling to find new ways to create electricity. All of the solutions we have found so far pose difficulties.

In the last century, we built dams in order to generate power. Most are still in use. Inside them, falling water turns turbines. This energy is clean and renewable. Nevertheless, dams harm fish and the people who depend on the fishing industry. Besides, they don't make enough electricity. Dams solved our energy problems for a while. However, they are not the answer for the future.

Coal, gas, oil, and nuclear power plants meet our power needs today. They heat water to create steam. The steam turns turbines. Unfortunately, these plants create pollution. They also use limited resources. This is a problem because someday we will run out of these fuels. Thermal plants are not the answer, either.

We will always need power, so we must look for other solutions. Solar panels create electricity from sunlight. Large fans change wind into power. Seaside plants harness wave energy. Geothermal plants tap the earth's natural heat. However, none of these sources has come close to meeting our needs. For now, the answer is conservation. Each of us must find ways to save electricity.

Comparing Electricity

Some electricity is generated by moving water. This is called hydroelectric power. Ocean wave power plants and special dams alike create this kind of power. In both, the force of moving water turns turbines.

Unlike hydroelectric power plants, thermal power plants move turbines with steam. Heat to create the steam is created by burning gas, oil, or coal. Similarly, steam turns turbines in nuclear power plants.

Some solar plants concentrate the heat of the sun with mirrors. They use that heat to boil water, like thermal power plants. Unlike those plants, solar plants use renewable energy and they do not create any waste. Unfortunately, they do not make as much electricity as nuclear or fossil fuel power plants.

Although most electricity is created using turbines, some is made in other ways. Special windmills turn generators in wind fields. Solar panels on roofs send electricity to homes and businesses. Like solar power plants, panels use the power of the sun. Although they work without creating pollution, they are not as dependable as fossil fuel power plants.

The Islands of Hawaii

From above, it is easy to see that Hawaii is unique. You cannot get there by car or drive across all of Hawaii. It is a chain of 132 islands. They look like a string of jewels in the blue Pacific Ocean.

Most are very small. The eight largest islands are located on the southeastern end of the group. The island of Hawaii is the biggest. Hawaiians call it the Big Island.

Each of the islands in the chain is really the top of a mountain. Of course, islands do not float on the water. They go all the way down to the ocean floor. The Pacific is deep, so these mountains are very tall.

If you fly over Hawaii at night, you might see glowing lava flowing from a cone-shaped peak. That is an active volcano. There are five of them on the Big Island.

Hawaiian Volcanoes

The Hawaiian Islands were formed by volcanoes. There is a hot spot on the ocean floor. When melted rock spurts up through the hot spot, it spills out on the seabed. Over time, the cooled rock builds up a cone-shaped mountain. Gradually, it gets taller. Finally, the volcano breaks the surface of the ocean. Then, an island is born.

The Pacific Plate is a chunk of the earth's crust. If it were staying still, there would only be one very tall island in the Hawaiian group. Actually, the plate, with the volcano riding on top of it, is moving all the time. When the plate moves, the hot spot stays still. Eventually, each volcano drifts away

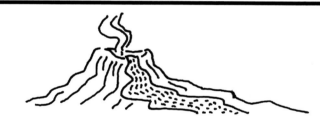

from the hot spot. Then, it stops erupting. Soon, the hot spot starts forming a new mountain on the seabed.

After a volcano becomes dormant, its peak starts to erode. Centuries of wind, rain, and waves have worn down most of the islands.

Today, only the volcanoes on the Big Island are over the hot spot. The next volcano, Loihi, is forming offshore. At the present time, its peak is still far below the ocean's surface. Someday, it may be part of the chain.